Lil Legends

BOOK OF CRAYON COLOURING

Vol. 6

Published by

Lil Legends

An imprint of Oswaal Books and Learning Private Limited

INDIA OFFICE

1/11, Sahitya Kunj, M.G. Road,
Agra - 282002, (UP) India

Phone: 0562-2857671
Email: contact@oswaalbooks.com
Website: www.OswaalBooks.com

ISBN: 978-93-59589-73-2 (Paperback)

Printed at: Kaveri Print Process Pvt. Ltd., Ecotech-*III*, G.Noida